# CELEBRATION SERIES®

## THE PIANO ODYSSEY®

PIANO
STUDIES / ETUDES

# 6

ISBN 0-88797-715-4

FREDERICK
HARRIS
MUSIC

# CELEBRATION SERIES®
## THE PIANO ODYSSEY®

The *Celebration Series®* was originally published in 1987 to international acclaim. In 1994, a second edition was released and received with heightened enthusiasm. Launched in 2001 and building on the success of previous editions, the *Celebration Series®, The Piano Odyssey®* takes advantage of the wealth of new repertoire and the changing interests and needs of teachers.

The series is breathtaking in its scope, presenting a true musical odyssey through the ages and their respective musical styles. The albums are graded from late elementary to early intermediate (albums Introductory to 3) through intermediate (albums 4 to 8) to advanced and concert repertoire (albums 9 and 10). Each volume of repertoire comprises a carefully selected grouping of pieces from the Baroque, Classical, Romantic, and 20th-century style periods. *Studies/Etudes* albums present compositions especially suited for building technique as well as musicality relevant to the repertoire of each level. *Student Workbooks* and recordings are available to assist in the study and enjoyment of the music. In addition, the comprehensive *Handbook for Teachers* is an invaluable pedagogical resource.

## A Note on Editing and Performance Practice

Most Baroque and early Classical composers wrote few dynamics, articulation, or other performance indications in their scores. Interpretation was left up to the performer, with the expectation that the performance practice was understood. In this edition, therefore, most of the dynamics and tempo indications in the Baroque and early Classical pieces have been added by the editors. These editorial markings, including fingering and the execution of ornaments, are intended to be helpful rather than definitive.

The keyboard instruments of the 17th and early 18th centuries lacked the sustaining power of the modern piano. Consequently, the usual keyboard touch was detached rather than legato. The pianist should assume that a lightly detached touch is appropriate for Baroque and early Classical music, unless a different approach is indicated by the style of the music.

Even into the 19th century, composers' scores could vary from copy to copy or edition to edition. Thus, the editors of the *Celebration Series®* have also made editorial choices in much of the Classical and Romantic repertoire presented in the series.

This edition follows the policy that the bar line cancels accidentals. In accordance with current practice, cautionary accidentals are added only in cases of possible ambiguity.

Teachers and students should refer to the companion guides – the *Student Workbooks* and the *Handbook for Teachers* – for further discussion of style and pedagogical elements. For examination requirements of The Royal Conservatory of Music, please refer to the current *Piano Syllabus*.

*Dr. Trish Sauerbrei*
Editor-in-Chief

# Contents

Study no. 1

# Prelude in C Minor
## BWV 999

Johann Sebastian Bach
(1685 – 1750)

Although originally written for the lute, this piece appears in numerous editions as a keyboard prelude.

0-88797-715-4 / 04

6

REMY

Study no. 2

# Toccatina
op. 27, no. 12

Dmitri Kabalevsky
(1904 – 1987)

Source: *Children's Pieces*, op. 27 (1937 – 1938)
Permission to reprint granted by G. Schirmer, Inc. (ASCAP); Boosey & Hawkes, Inc.; Internationale Musikverlage
Hans Sikorski; Le Chant du Monde; and Zenon Music Company Ltd. for their respective territories.

Study no. 3

# Entrée in G Minor
## HWV 453

George Frideric Handel
(1685 – 1759)

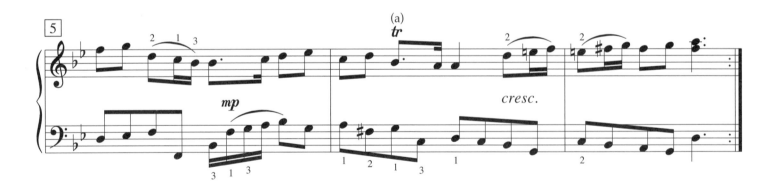

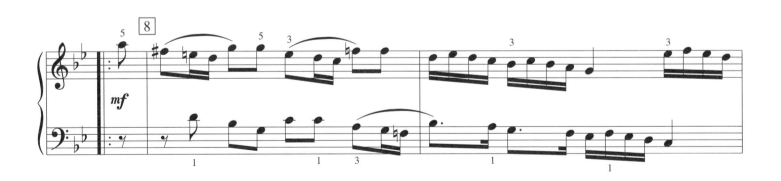

Most eighth notes may be played detached.

0-88797-715-4 / 08

Study no. 4

# Study in E Minor
## op. 132, no. 1

Cornelius Gurlitt
(1820 – 1901)

Study no. 5

# Barcarole
op. 138, no. 5

Stephen Heller
(1813 – 1888)

Source: *Notenbuch für Klein und Gross*, op. 38 (Bonn, 1874)

PASCAL.

Study no. 6

# Toccatina

Ruth Watson Henderson
(1932 –      )

Source: *Six Miniatures for Piano*

© Copyright 1994 The Frederick Harris Music Co., Limited, Mississauga, Ontario, Canada.

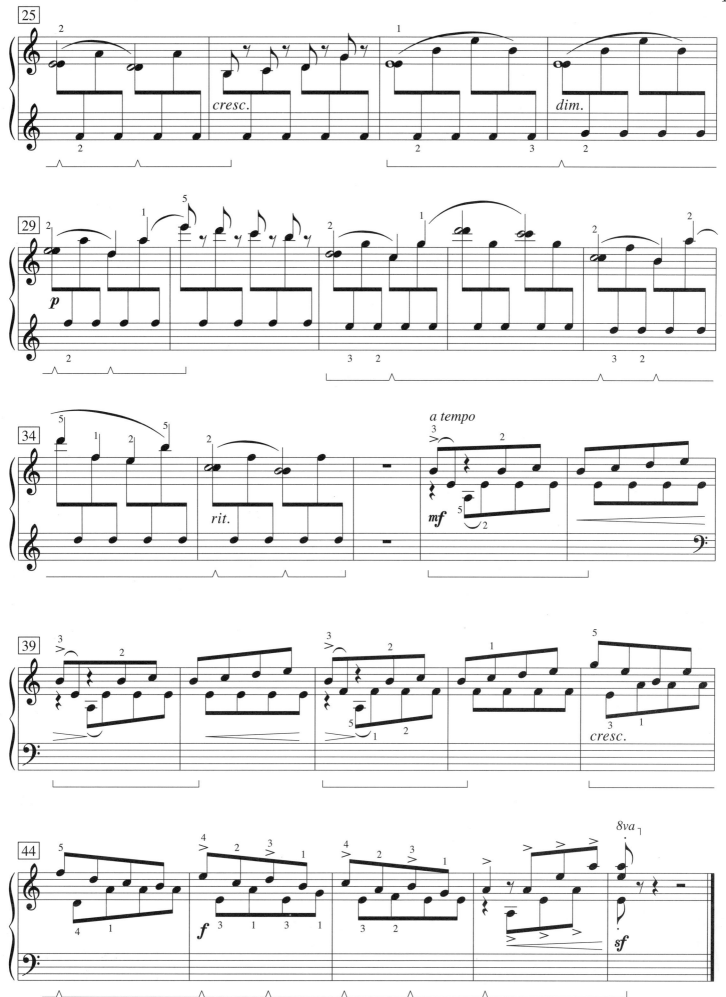

# Study in E Minor

**Study no. 7**

op. 29, no. 14

Henri Bertini
(1798 – 1876)

Study no. 8

# Fluttering Leaves
op. 46, no. 11

Stephen Heller
(1813 – 1888)

Source: *30 Études progressives* (Berlin, 1844)

0-88797-715-4 / 15

NADINE

Study no. 9

# Dance

Dmitri Shostakovich
(1906 – 1975)

sempre staccato

cresc.

Source: *Puppet Dances* (1952 – 1962)
Permission to reprint granted by G. Schirmer, Inc. (ASCAP); Boosey & Hawkes, Inc.; Internationale Musikverlage
Hans Sikorski; Le Chant du Monde; MMI-Harmony at RAO; and Zenon Music Company Ltd. for their respective
territories.

Study no. 10

# Abenddämmerung

*Dusk*

op. 138, no. 3

Stephen Heller
(1813 – 1888)

Source: *Notenbuch für Klein und Gross*, op. 138 (Bonn, 1874)

Study no. 11

# Playing Ball

Ross Lee Finney
(1906 – 1997)

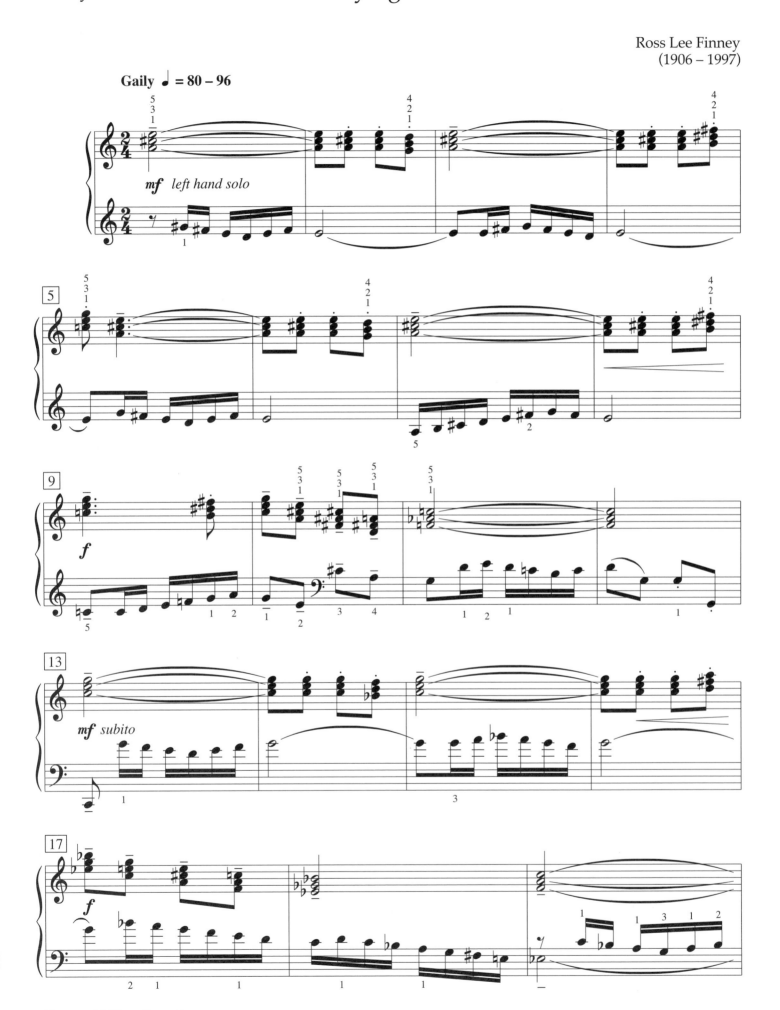

Source: *24 Piano Inventions*

© Copyright 1971 Henmar Press Inc. Reprinted by permission of C.F. Peters Corporation, New York.

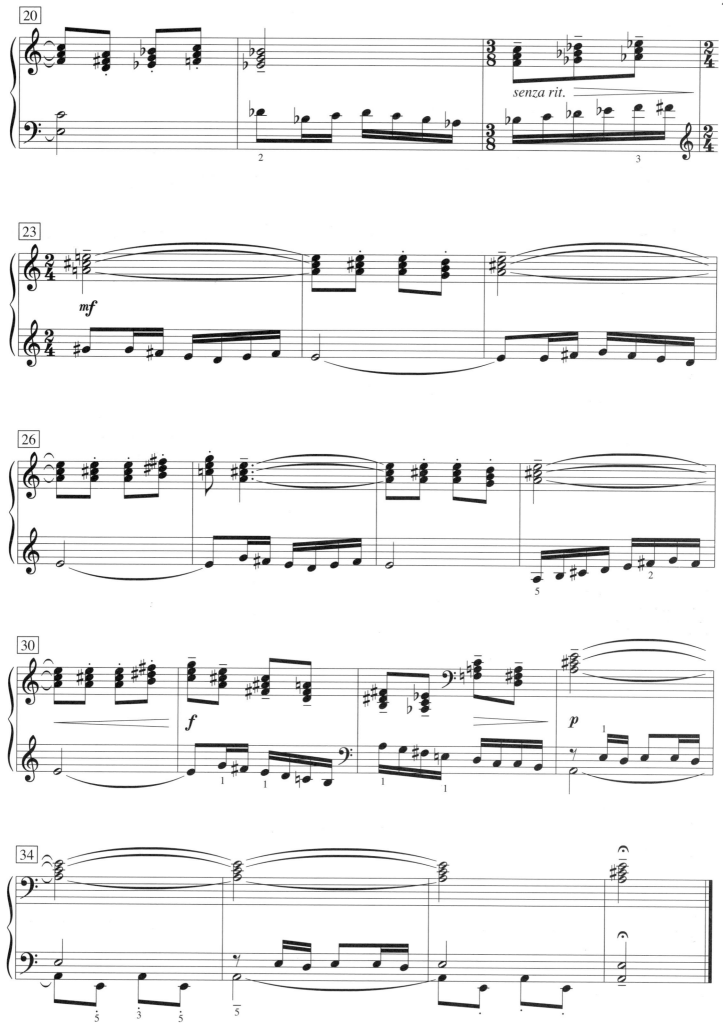

Study no. 12

# A Little Song

op. 47, no. 4

Robert Fuchs
(1847 – 1927)

**Langsam, gesangvoll** \*  ♩. = 66 – 72

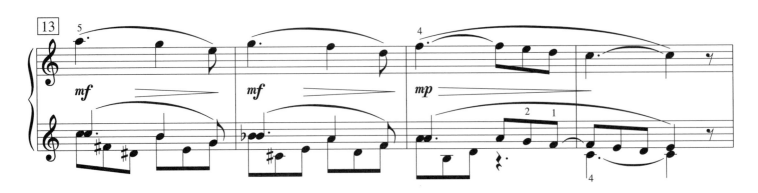

Original title: "Liedchen"

\* Slowly, singing

Source: *Jugend-Album*, op. 47 (1890)

0-88797-715-4 / 22

Study no. 13

# Game of Patience

op. 25, no. 2

Génari Karganov
(1858 – 1890)

"Patience" is the name of a card game.

Source: *Jugend-Album*, op. 25